Theory Paper   Grade 1   2018   A

Duration 1½ hours

Candidates should answer ALL questions.
Write your answers on this paper – no others will be accepted.
Answers must be written clearly and neatly – otherwise marks may be lost.

TOTAL MARKS
100

1 (a) Add the time signature to each of these three examples.

10

(b) Add the missing bar-lines to this melody. The first bar-line is given.

2 Add a rest at the places marked ∗ in these two melodies to make each bar complete.

10

3 Answer **both** (a) and (b).

(a) Give the letter name of each of the notes marked ∗, including the flat sign where necessary.
The first answer is given.

C
....

(b) Give the time name (e.g. quaver or
eighth note) of the rest in the last bar. ....

4 Name the key of each of these scales. Also draw a bracket (⌐⌐) over each pair of notes
making a semitone, as shown in the first scale.

Key ....

Key ....

Key ....

5 (a) Draw a circle around the **higher** note of each of these pairs of notes.

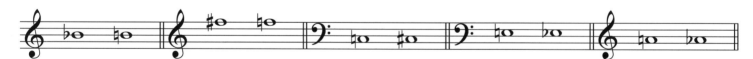

(b) Draw a circle around the **lower** note of each of these pairs of notes.

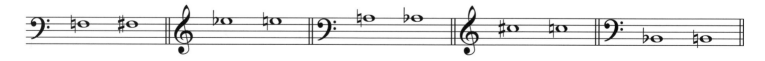

6 Write the dynamics *mf* *pp* *ff* *mp* *p* *f* in the correct order, from the **loudest** to the **quietest**. The first answer is given.

| 10 |

ff ....

7 Add the correct clef to make each of these named notes, as shown in the first answer.

| 10 |

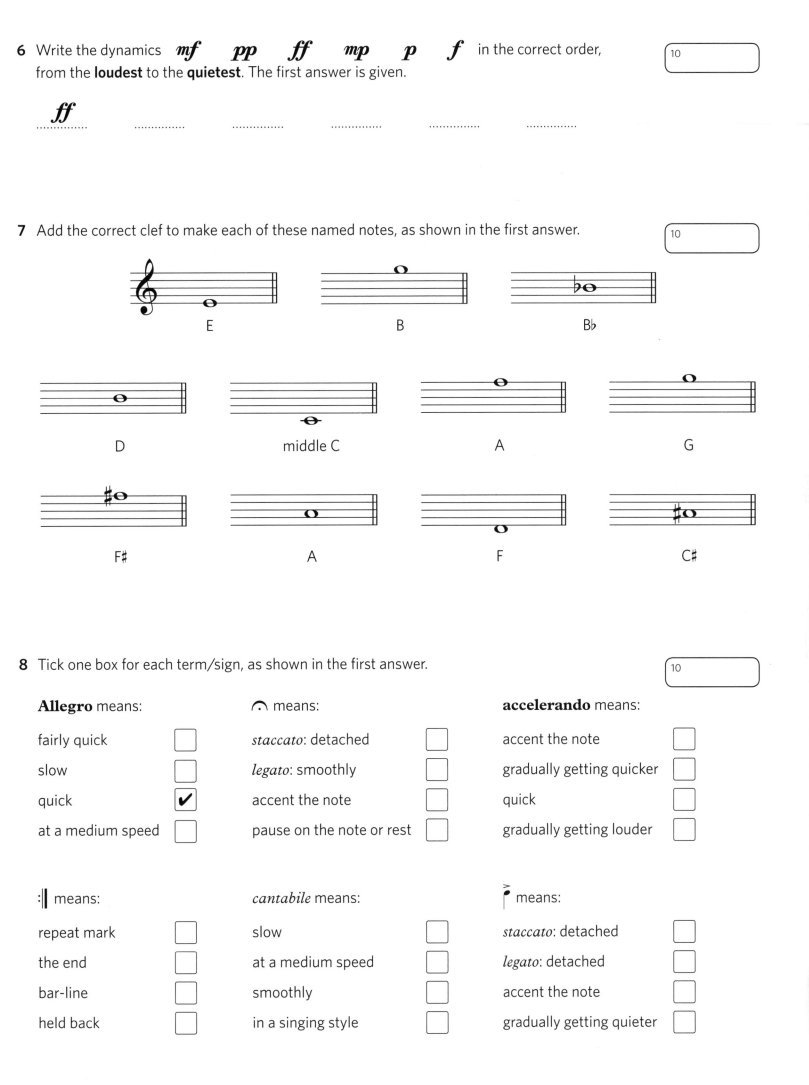

E   B   Bb

D   middle C   A   G

F#   A   F   C#

8 Tick one box for each term/sign, as shown in the first answer.

| 10 |

Allegro means:

fairly quick	☐
slow	☐
quick	✔
at a medium speed	☐

⌢ means:

staccato: detached	☐
legato: smoothly	☐
accent the note	☐
pause on the note or rest	☐

accelerando means:

accent the note	☐
gradually getting quicker	☐
quick	☐
gradually getting louder	☐

:‖ means:

repeat mark	☐
the end	☐
bar-line	☐
held back	☐

cantabile means:

slow	☐
at a medium speed	☐
smoothly	☐
in a singing style	☐

> means:

staccato: detached	☐
legato: detached	☐
accent the note	☐
gradually getting quieter	☐

9 Look at this melody and then answer the questions below.

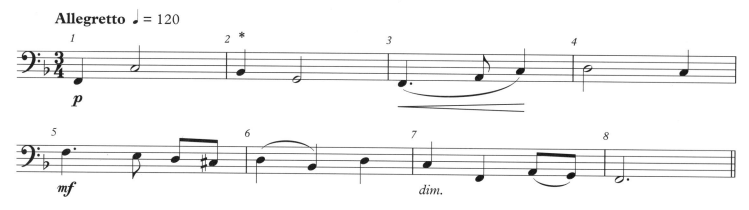

Write your answer to question (b) on the stave below.

(a) (i) The melody is in the key of F major. Give the number of a
 bar that contains **all** the notes of the tonic triad in this key.   Bar ....

 10

(ii) Name the degree of the scale (e.g. 2nd, 3rd, 4th) of the
 first note in bar 2 (marked *). Remember that the key is F major.   ....

(iii) Answer TRUE or FALSE to these sentences:

 All the notes in bar 5 can be found in the key of F major.   ....

 ♩ = 120 means 120 crotchets (quarter notes) in a bar.   ....

(iv) Give the time name (e.g. crotchet or
 quarter note) of the **longest** note in the melody.   ....

(b) Copy out the music from the start of bar 5 to the end of bar 8, exactly as it is written above.
 Don't forget the clef, key signature, dynamics and all other details. Write the music on the
 blank stave above question (a).

 10

Theory Paper   Grade 1   2018   B

Duration 1½ hours

Candidates should answer ALL questions.
Write your answers on this paper – no others will be accepted.
Answers must be written clearly and neatly – otherwise marks may be lost.

1   Add the missing bar-lines to these two melodies. The first bar-line is given in each.   [10]

2   Add the correct clef to make each of these named notes, as shown in the first answer.   [10]

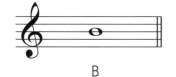   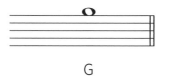   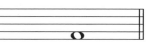

B   F#   G

         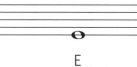

C#   B♭   D   A

F   middle C   G   E

3 (a) Draw a circle around the **higher** note of each of these pairs of notes.

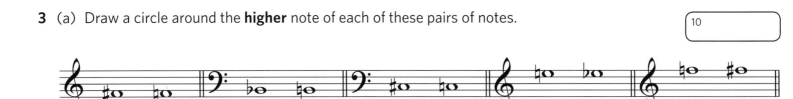

(b) Draw a circle around the **lower** note of each of these pairs of notes.

4 Name the major keys shown by these key signatures. The first answer is given.

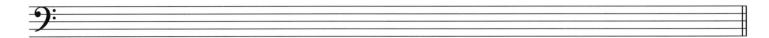

......D major......

....

....

....

....

....

5 Using semibreves (whole notes), write one octave of the scales named below.
Do **not** use key signatures, but remember to add any necessary accidentals.

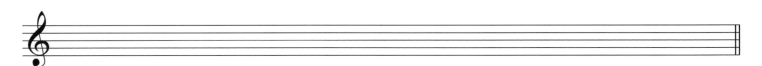

C major, ascending

D major, descending

8

6 Add a rest at the places marked ∗ in these two melodies to make each bar complete.

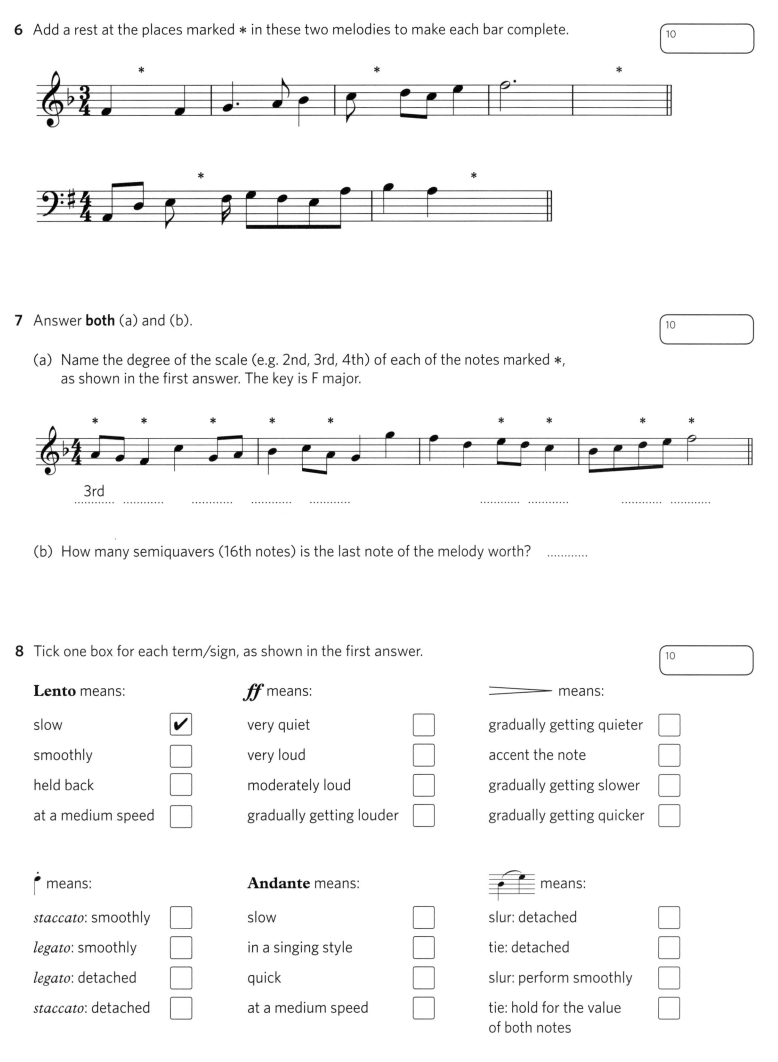

7 Answer **both** (a) and (b).

10

(a) Name the degree of the scale (e.g. 2nd, 3rd, 4th) of each of the notes marked ∗, as shown in the first answer. The key is F major.

3rd

(b) How many semiquavers (16th notes) is the last note of the melody worth? ....

8 Tick one box for each term/sign, as shown in the first answer.

10

Lento means:

slow ✔
smoothly ☐
held back ☐
at a medium speed ☐

ff means:

very quiet ☐
very loud ☐
moderately loud ☐
gradually getting louder ☐

⟋ means:

gradually getting quieter ☐
accent the note ☐
gradually getting slower ☐
gradually getting quicker ☐

⸰ means:

staccato: smoothly ☐
legato: smoothly ☐
legato: detached ☐
staccato: detached ☐

Andante means:

slow ☐
in a singing style ☐
quick ☐
at a medium speed ☐

⌒ means:

slur: detached ☐
tie: detached ☐
slur: perform smoothly ☐
tie: hold for the value of both notes ☐

9 Look at this melody and then answer the questions below.

Write your answer to question (b) on the stave below.

(a) (i) Give the letter name of the **highest** note in the melody. ....

10

(ii) The melody is in the key of D major. Give the number of
a bar that contains **all** the notes of the tonic triad in this key. Bar ....

(iii) How many bars contain a dotted crotchet (dotted quarter note)? ....

(iv) In which bar is the player told to pause or hold on to a note? Bar ....

(v) Answer TRUE or FALSE to this sentence:

The lower **4** in **4/4** means crotchet (quarter-note) beats in a bar. ....

(b) Copy out the music from the start of bar 1 to the end of bar 3, exactly as it is written above.
Don't forget the clef, key signature, time signature, tempo marking, dynamics and all other
details. Write the music on the blank stave above question (a).

10

Theory Paper   Grade 1   2018   C

Duration 1½ hours

Candidates should answer ALL questions.
Write your answers on this paper – no others will be accepted.
Answers must be written clearly and neatly – otherwise marks may be lost.

TOTAL MARKS
100

1 Add the missing bar-lines to these two melodies. The first bar-line is given in each.

2 Answer **both** (a) and (b).

10

(a) Give the letter name of each of the notes marked ∗, including the sharp sign where necessary.
    The first answer is given.

(b) How many bars contain a dotted crotchet (dotted quarter note)?   ....

3 Name the major keys shown by these key signatures. The first answer is given.

[10]

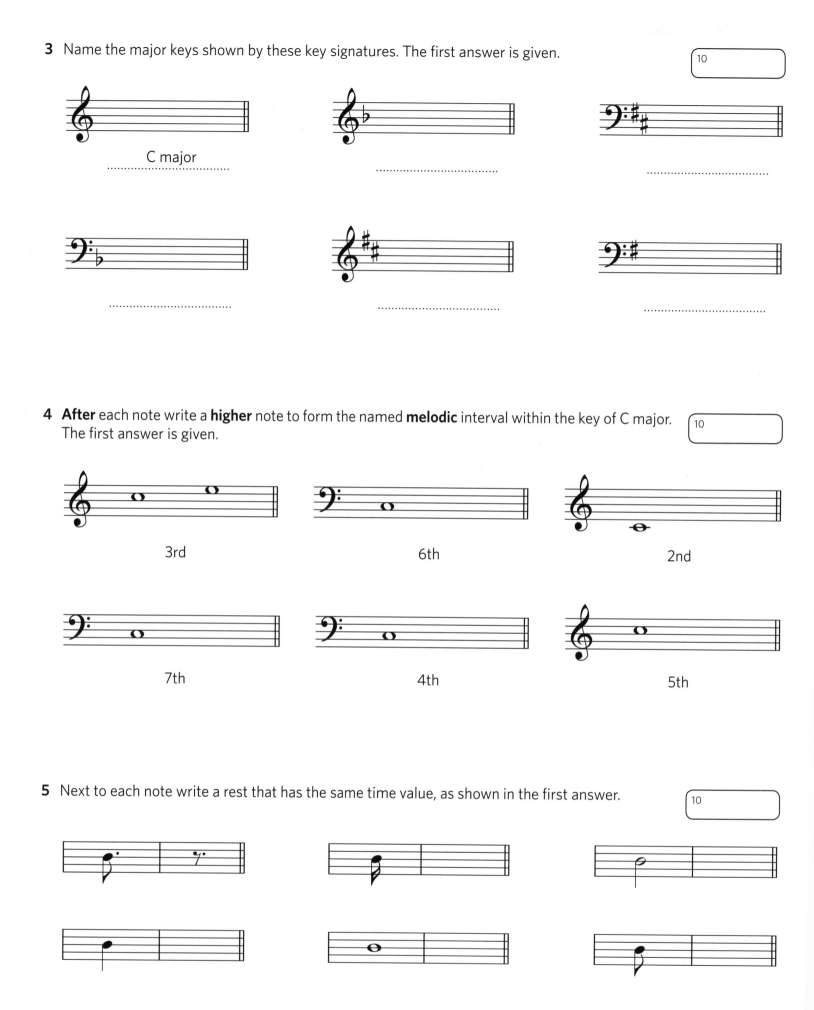

C major

....

....

....

....

....

4 **After** each note write a **higher** note to form the named **melodic** interval within the key of C major.
The first answer is given.

[10]

3rd

6th

2nd

7th

4th

5th

5 Next to each note write a rest that has the same time value, as shown in the first answer.

[10]

6 Add the correct clef and any necessary accidentals to make each of the scales named below. Do **not** use key signatures.

F major

G major

7 Write the time values ♩ ♩ 𝅝 ♪ ♪ ♩. in the correct order, from the **longest** to the **shortest**. The first answer is given.

𝅝
....

8 Tick one box for each term/sign, as shown in the first answer.

means:

slur: perform smoothly	☐
tie: detached	☐
slur: detached	☐
tie: hold for the value of both notes	✔

legato means:

slow	☐
very quiet	☐
detached	☐
smoothly	☐

Allegretto means:

slow	☐
fairly quick	☐
gradually getting slower	☐
gradually getting quicker	☐

cresc. means:

gradually getting louder	☐
gradually getting slower	☐
loud	☐
gradually getting quieter	☐

p means:

loud	☐
quiet	☐
moderately quiet	☐
very loud	☐

Fine means:

in time	☐
a little	☐
the end	☐
repeat from the beginning	☐

9 Look at this melody and then answer the questions below.

Write your answer to question (b) on the stave below.

(a) (i) The melody is in the key of G major. Name the degree of
the scale (e.g. 4th, 5th, 6th) of the first note of the melody. ....

(ii) Answer TRUE or FALSE to these sentences:

Bar 3 contains **all** the notes of the tonic triad of G major. ....

The music gets gradually faster in bar 7. ....

(iii) Give the time name (e.g. crotchet or
quarter note) of the **longest** note in the melody. ....

(iv) How many quavers (eighth notes)
is the first note of the melody worth? ....

(b) Copy out the music from the start of bar 1 to the end of bar 4, exactly as it is written above.
Don't forget the clef, key signature, time signature, tempo marking, dynamics and all other
details. Write the music on the blank stave above question (a).

Theory Paper   Grade 1   2018   S

TOTAL MARKS
100

Duration 1½ hours

Candidates should answer ALL questions.
Write your answers on this paper – no others will be accepted.
Answers must be written clearly and neatly – otherwise marks may be lost.

1 (a) Add the time signature to each of these three examples.

10

(b) Add a rest at each of the two places marked * to make the bars complete.

2 Write the dynamics   **ff**   **pp**   **mp**   **f**   **p**   **mf**   in the correct order, from the **quietest** to the **loudest**. The first answer is given.

10

pp
....

3 Answer **both** (a) and (b).

(a) Add the correct clef to each of these tonic triads.

C major   G major

Letter names   ....

(b) Under each triad write the letter name of each note.

4 (a) Draw a circle around the **higher** note of each of these pairs of notes.

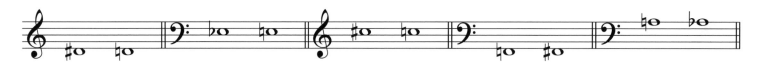

(b) Draw a circle around the **lower** note of each of these pairs of notes.

5 Name the key of each of these scales. Also draw a bracket (⌐¬) over each pair of notes making a semitone, as shown in the first scale.

Key   ....

Key   ....

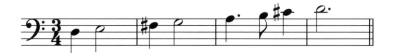

Key   ....